"Essential Food Hygiene"

Dr. R. J. Donaldson OBE

First published in 1988 by The Royal Society of Health, RSH House, 38A St George's Drive, London SW1V 4BH. Tel: 071 630 0121

Reprinted 1989 with additional information including a revised and safer definition of the temperature Danger Zone (5°C-63°C)

Reprinted 1991
(ref 91/1/A1): updated graph illustrating cases of food poisoning in England and Wales (Source: CDSC)
(ref 91/2/A2): with updated figure for known cases of food poisoning in 1988.
(ref 91/3/A2) : (ref 91/4/A2) : (ref 91/5/A2) : (ref 91/6/A2) : (ref 91/8/A2)

The Royal Society of Health

London

1

ACKNOWLEDGEMENTS

I acknowledge, with thanks, the help in developing the booklet received from the following members of the Working Party set up by the Royal Society of Health to introduce a new certificate course in Essential Food Hygiene:

Mr G S Wiggins — Chairman
Mr W Bate, MBE
Mr H A Ackroyd
Mr P Povey
Mr W B Twyford

Pertinent comments from Mr G Coleman and Mr D White of Llantech Environmental Services Ltd were of great help. Some of the drawings are taken from the teaching pack which the Society commissioned from them.

Rosemary Probert and Ray Clancy illuminated the text with some light-hearted drawings.

The work of Bob Campbell in formatting the draft and organising the printing is much appreciated.

I was particularly fortunate in having as a research assistant John Randall who made a substantial contribution to the development of the booklet, including typing of many drafts and the final design.

Blackfords of Cornwall
Tel: (0726) 63638

Contents

Introduction

Essential Food Hygiene has been written at a time when there is widespread and well founded concern about food poisoning.

Food is essential to life but if contaminated it can cause illness — even death. Within recent memory, nineteen people in a hospital died as a result of eating food that looked, smelled and even tasted quite normal but which had become poisonous through carelessness.

Fortunately, only a minority of food poisoning cases lead to death but many cause unpleasant and weakening illnesses.

The sad truth is that food poisoning is an ever growing problem, with more and more people suffering its effects each year. The danger lies in the ease with which it can strike: the cause is almost always human error. It does not happen by accident, but occurs when people **store, handle,** or **prepare** food incorrectly.

Yet there is no reason why this should be so. Food poisoning can be prevented just as easily as it can be caused, by taking the time and care to follow the basic rules of food hygiene that are outlined in this booklet. These rules apply equally to the workplace and to the home.

Food poisoning is a formidable enemy:
knowledge is our best defence.

That is why this booklet has been written.

A Historical Note

This section briefly outlines the history of our current understanding of food poisoning and points out that in spite of modern scientific knowledge, many mistakes are made.

EARLY TIMES

Concern about what food is edible and what food is not, has its origins in ancient times. The Old Testament of The Bible contains laws laid down by Moses not only about which animals were fit for human consumption but also about cleanliness in general. Much of this was based on practical knowledge. Food poisoning as a disease entity has been recognised for centuries.

BACTERIA THE KEY

However, it was only about 100 years ago that the scientific basis as to the cause of communicable diseases, including food poisoning, became known when the famous French chemist, Pasteur, demonstrated that bacteria could cause disease. He also disproved the old and longstanding theory of "spontaneous generation" which maintained that bacteria could form naturally in fluids. At about the same time, the German physician Robert Koch was making similar discoveries, and recognised that bacteria were responsible for a number of diseases, including cholera.

The dawning of this scientific era required a public education programme to dispel the myths and misconceptions, and also to persuade reluctant government bodies to take action.

In these campaigns, the Royal Society of Health took a leading role to promote health and improve the social conditions of the times. It was formed in 1876, and 6 years later Queen Victoria — who displayed great interest in the health of her people — became its patron, and the prefix "Royal" was granted in 1904 by King Edward the Seventh.

For centuries there have been accounts of people becoming ill after eating food. This was thought to be due to chemical poisons — sometimes added deliberately. Later a chemical substance called ptomaine, which is formed in protein-food during putrification, was implicated. Even today one can come across references to ptomaine poisoning. Eventually, when ptomaine was extracted from food, it was found to be harmless when taken by mouth.

THE LINK

The definitive link with bacteria as a cause of food poisoning came in 1888. A German doctor named Gaertner isolated bacteria from the organs of a man who had died in a food poisoning outbreak. He found identical bacteria in the left-over meat that the man and his companions had consumed as well as in the carcass from which the meat had come. Thus the cause was established. It was also gradually realised that food could be heavily contaminated with bacteria, and yet smell and taste the same as normal food.

By the beginning of this century, food had become more plentiful and cheap, and the small eating-houses of the day were often very insanitary. Paradoxically, there were few reports of food poisoning outbreaks, possibly because of the small number of people involved. However, the more likely explanation is that the meat was cooked and served immediately to the customers, unlike the mass-catering of today when food is cooked and sometimes held, unfortunately, at the temperature at which bacteria can grow.

A CAUTIONARY TALE

During the last 100 years more groups of bacteria have been implicated in food poisoning, and new types have been imported.

For example, during World War Two, when this country was very dependent upon imported food, dried-egg from the U.S.A. was popular. Some of this dried-egg contained small numbers of food poisoning bacteria. The illness was caused by the method of preparation and cooking. What often happened was that the housewife would make the mixture of dried-egg and milk the night before, and leave it in the warm kitchen and next morning cook it quickly and lightly for her husband going to work the early shift. Hence the bacteria were provided with the nutrients, warmth, moisture and time to grow profusely, and the cooking process was inadequate to destroy them all. Thus new members of the families of food poisoning bacteria were introduced into war-time Britain.

Unfortunately many of the outbreaks of food poisoning today still relate to similar mistakes, when the "high risk" foods are held for too long within the temperature "Danger Zone". These problems are discussed in more detail later in the booklet.

Food Poisoning

This important section defines food poisoning, and provides the profoundly depressing facts about the increasing number of cases.

DEFINITION

Food poisoning can be broadly defined as those conditions caused by the ingestion of food or drink, in which the main symptoms are diarrhoea and vomiting, singularly or together, and usually accompanied by nausea ("feeling sick") and stomach pains.

The onset of symptoms is usually sudden and may start within 2 hours of taking the food, but there may be an interval of up to 2 days. The illness can last 1 or 2 days, but sometimes can continue for a week or more.

THE INCIDENCE OF FOOD POISONING

Food poisoning strikes thousands of people every year, the total number of new cases being called the **incidence** of food poisoning.

In 1988 alone, there were approximately 40,000 known cases of the illness in England and Wales. These figures represent only the tip of the iceberg because many cases are not reported.

This is all profoundly depressing, for the incidence of food poisoning has been rising steadily since World War II.

Among the reasons for this increase is the heightened popularity of eating out. Poor standards in the household kitchen have consequences only for the family, but the same mistakes in the kitchen of a canteen or restaurant can cause illness amongst a very large number of people. In addition, there is a tendency to buy made-up meat dishes for home consumption and these have been incriminated in outbreaks of food poisoning.

Another explanation for the increased incidence of food poisoning is a general, and regrettable, laxity in standards of hygiene, together with a lack of understanding of the principles involved in handling and preparing food safely.

There is general agreement that one of the main strategies of prevention of food poisoning lies in **better education** of the workers involved, and thus an adoption of good practices in the work place.

CASES OF FOOD POISONING IN ENGLAND AND WALES

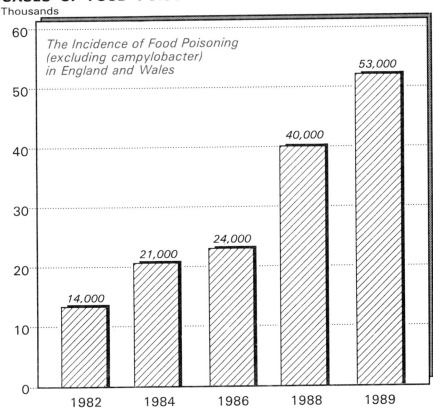

Thousands

The Incidence of Food Poisoning (excluding campylobacter) in England and Wales

Causes of Food Poisoning

This important section stresses that bacteria are the most common cause of food poisoning in Britain, and also mentions the less important causes.

BACTERIA

Bacteria are tiny living creatures, so small that you cannot see them with the naked eye, but they are all around us and on and in our bodies.

Most bacteria are harmless and some are even helpful to man. But there is a small, important, proportion which can infect some foods when conditions are suitable and cause food poisoning.

Certain diseases, like typhoid and tuberculosis for instance, can be transmitted by food which carries the appropriate bacteria — often in relatively small numbers. Although these bacteria cause disease when they are eaten in food, they are quite different from food poisoning bacteria.

In this booklet we shall be concerned mainly with bacteria which cause food poisoning, because they are by far the most common cause of food poisoning, and because the methods used to prevent the contamination of food by bacteria will generally work to prevent contamination from other sources.

It is these food poisoning bacteria that we will be considering in more detail, but first we will refer briefly to some other less frequent causes of contamination.

VIRUSES

Viruses are tiny particles — even smaller than bacteria — which can be seen only with a special microscope. They grow only in living tissue, thus cannot grow in food. The part they play in causing food poisoning is not fully understood.

OTHER POISONS

Occasionally chemical poisons can get into food from cooking utensils — particularly with acid foods — or accidentally from weed killers and insecticides. Fruit sprayed with pesticides may also cause chemical food poisoning. It is advisable therefore to wash fruit before it is eaten.

Poisoning can result from eating poisonous plants or fungi, such as toadstools, poisonous berries or seeds, such as those of the laburnum tree. Children are more likely to suffer such poisoning.

These other poisons are infrequent causes of food poisoning and will not be discussed in any detail in this booklet.

NOTE:

Allergies

Some people may suffer symptoms as a result of eating certain foods, simply because they happen to be sensitive to those particular foods—in the same way that hay fever sufferers are sensitive to pollen during the summer.

This is called an allergic reaction, and individuals who eat foods for which they have an allergy may suffer from vomiting and diarrhoea, even though the food is fit to eat. Shellfish, strawberries and cheese are examples of foods to which people are occasionally allergic. Generally, people who have allergies become aware of foods they should avoid.

Allergic reactions are uncommon and are not the result of food being contaminated.

Bacteria

This important section describes bacteria as small living creatures which require food, moisture, warmth and time to grow.

THE NATURE OF BACTERIA

Bacteria are tiny living creatures, often known as "germs". They are so small that it is impossible to see them without a microscope. They are usually round or rod-shaped.

Bacteria are EVERYWHERE. . .

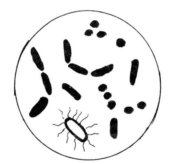

. . .in soil, dust, and water, in the air around us, and on our bodies

Food poisoning bacteria seen through a microscope

Of the many different types of bacteria only a small number are responsible for food poisoning; indeed, some are beneficial, helping to make cheese and yoghurt.

But it is the dangerous food-poisoning bacteria which concern us most.

HOW BACTERIA GROW

It is important to remember that just like us, bacteria are living things, and that in the same way as we need water and food to survive, so bacteria also need them.

To live and grow, bacteria must have the following FOUR conditions:

★ FOOD ★ MOISTURE ★ WARMTH ★ TIME

FOOD

Not all food is suitable for bacterial growth. Food containing sugar, salt, and acid — such as jam or pickles — will discourage the growth of bacteria.

What is important for you to remember are those foods that encourage and allow bacteria to grow — and these are referred to as **"high risk"** foods. The following are the main categories:—

● meat and poultry

ALL meat and poultry products provide the conditions for bacterial growth

Raw meat, and particularly raw poultry, may be soiled by the contents of the animal's intestine. It has been shown that some 80% of frozen chickens contain food poisoning bacteria

● cooked meat and gravy, soups, stocks

Cooked meat and gravy, soups and stocks provide the nutrients that bacteria need to grow. If kept under warm conditions, a small number of bacteria will become many millions in a short time

● milk and eggs

Milk and eggs, and food containing milk and eggs (such as cream, custard, or mayonnaise) are often involved in cases of food poisoning, nearly always because they have been handled incorrectly

● raw shellfish and seafood

Prawns, mussels, crabs or lobsters may eat food that is contaminated, or they may pick up food poisoning bacteria from polluted water. For example, shellfish such as oysters could have been taken from sewage polluted waters

● cooked rice

Cooked rice may contain bacteria that has survived the cooking process and these will grow rapidly if stored for sufficient time in warm conditions

> **PAY SPECIAL ATTENTION TO THE HIGH RISK FOODS**

MOISTURE

Bacteria need water. They can grow only in food that contains moisture, and so they are less likely to survive in dried foods, such as powdered milk or dried eggs.

Unfortunately some bacteria do survive under such dry conditions. Hence when fluids are added to the food, they begin to grow again. The story of dried eggs has already been mentioned in the history section.

Outbreaks of food poisoning have been traced to rice that has been cooked and stored under warm conditions before being re-heated and served.

A bacterium known as **Bacillus cereus** has been found in dried rice. Some of these bacteria can survive cooking. If the cooked rice is allowed to remain at a warm temperature the bacteria will grow profusely and produce a toxin (poison) which can withstand heat for a considerable time.

Thus, once the toxin has been produced in the cooked rice, the normal process of re-heating will be of little use.

WARMTH

The temperatures referred to throughout the booklet are in degrees Celsius (°C).

Bacteria which cause food poisoning will grow most quickly at a temperature around 37°C, which is the normal temperature of the human body, but as long as food is warm — at temperatures between 5°C and 63°C — they will continue to grow.

For this reason, the range of temperatures between **5°C and 63°C**, is known as the

> **DANGER ZONE**

Even a small number of bacteria can grow rapidly in food if it is allowed to remain in the Danger Zone, making the food dangerous to eat.

Temperatures outside the Danger Zone, however, are less suitable for bacteria. Most bacteria are killed at 75°C during a cooking process of between 10–30 minutes. It is important to remember that this temperature must be reached at the centre of the food. However, some bacteria and their toxins (poisons) require higher temperatures for a longer period of time before they are destroyed.

In cold conditions, below 5°C, the growth of bacteria virtually ceases. At very low temperatures, some will die, but many will survive and grow again in warm conditions.

Temperatures and bacterial growth

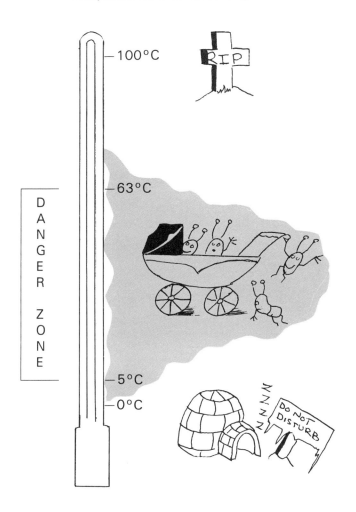

TIME

Given moist warm food, bacteria simply need time to grow. It is often carelessness that allows them the time they need, such as when food is allowed to remain in the Danger Zone.

Each bacterial cell multiplies, or reproduces, by splitting itself in two, so that 1 bacterial cell becomes **2** bacterial cells. Each of these 2 bacteria then split to make **4** bacteria. Each of the 4 bacteria split into two again, making **8** bacteria, and so on.

Bacteria will reproduce in this way every **10–20 minutes**, at a suitable temperature for growth.

This means that after reproducing at this rate for only 24 hours, **one bacterium will have given rise to about 7000 million bacteria**.

The four conditions required for the growth of bacteria

Warmth   **Moisture**

Food   **Time**

How bacteria cause food poisoning

This important section explains the way bacteria act to produce symptoms and gives the main sources of these bacteria.

BACTERIA AND FOOD POISONING

A large number of bacteria are needed to produce symptoms, so they require time and the right conditions to grow. There are a number of different kinds of food poisoning bacteria, each having its own name, but **Salmonella** is the name given to the family of bacteria that is responsible for a large proportion of the reported food poisoning outbreaks in the United Kingdom.

(The term Salmonella comes from the name of the American vet — Dr. Salmon — who in 1885 was the first to isolate this family of bacteria.)

Bacteria cause food poisoning in different ways, but their behaviour depends on the type of bacteria they are. Their various names tend to be long and often difficult to pronounce but there is no need for you to remember the individual names so long as you understand how they create their havoc.

Bacteria cause food poisoning in one of three ways:-

● bacteria which grow throughout the food in large numbers, so that when we eat the food, we eat the bacteria too

For example, a small number of **Salmonella** bacteria could be transferred from someone's hands to suitable (high risk) food and, if given sufficient time at the right temperature, many millions of bacteria could grow, and then be eaten.

● bacteria which are difficult to kill with heat

A good example of this is a bacterium with the long name **Clostridium perfringens,** which is often found in raw meat and poultry. It has the capacity to change into a resistant form called spores. Some of these spores can survive the normal cooking process. A joint of meat in which a few spores have survived cooking, if left to **cool slowly** in a warm kitchen, can result in the spores changing back into the usual form of bacteria which then grow very rapidly.

● bacteria which release their toxins in the food before the food is eaten

One such bacterium is called **Staphylococcus aureus** (found in the nose, throat and infected wounds) which can produce poisons in custards and trifles, as well as in cooked meat and poultry. . . if allowed time to grow in warm conditions.

SOURCES OF FOOD POISONING BACTERIA

Before you can protect food from bacteria you need to know where the bacteria come from, and how they come to be present in the food we eat. Most come from man and animal sources.

Raw meat and poultry

Many bacteria, including two of those we have just discussed — salmonella and clostridium perfringens — live in the intestines, or "gut", of both animals and human beings. The animals concerned usually have no symptoms, and just carry the bacteria. Thus they can be transferred to meat intended for human consumption.

For this reason, it is wise to think of all raw meat and poultry products, as well as the juices that come from them, as already carrying many food poisoning bacteria before they arrive in the kitchen; raw meat, and particularly raw poultry, are frequent sources of food poisoning outbreaks.

The human body

Bacteria which can cause food poisoning are carried in several areas of your own body — for example, the previously noted staphylococcus aureus, found on your hands and skin, in your nose, throat, mouth, ears, hair and fingernails. As already mentioned, bacteria which cause food poisoning, such as salmonella, can also be present in our intestines, and thus in faeces (stools). People with these bacteria often have no symptoms, and are referred to as carriers.

Careless food-handling is one of the most common causes of bacterial infection — with bacteria being carried on hands, from the mouth, nose and faeces, or in infected cuts, grazes, scratches or boils.

SOURCES OF FOOD POISONING BACTERIA

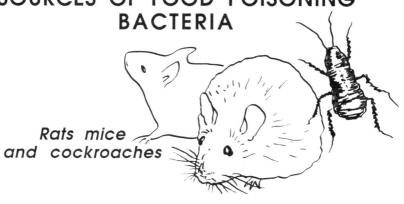

Rats mice and cockroaches

Raw meat and poultry

Food handlers

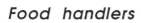

Waste food and dirt

WAYS IN WHICH STAPHYLOCOCCUS AUREUS ENTERS FOOD

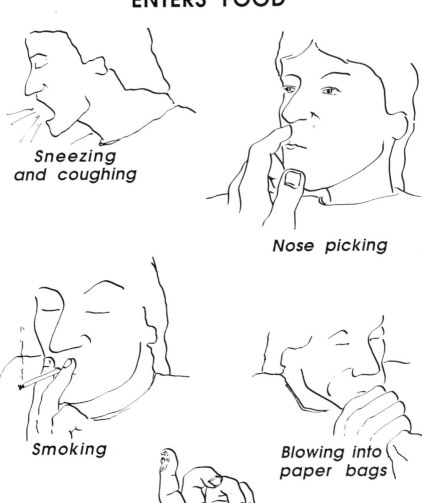

Sneezing and coughing

Nose picking

Smoking

Blowing into paper bags

Handling food when you have a septic cut

A way in which salmonella get into food

From our gut due to handling food after using the toilet

Other sources within the environment

Creatures such as flies and other insects, rats and mice, and animals like cats and dogs are likely to come into close contact with food poisoning bacteria in the places they inhabit, or through the kind of food they eat.

Carrying bacteria on their bodies, or in their urine and droppings, they can enter kitchens from the outside — either through cracks, ventilation openings, open doors and windows, or with deliveries to the kitchen.

Finally, waste food and rubbish provide ideal conditions in which bacteria can live and reproduce, because they are warm, and often are left undisturbed for several hours.

Hygiene Control

This important section gives details of action you should take to prevent food becoming contaminated.

DEFINITION OF FOOD HYGIENE

Food hygiene is the action taken to ensure that food is handled, stored, prepared and served in such a way, and under such conditions, as to prevent — as far as possible — the contamination of the food.

Food poisoning is the final link in a chain of circumstances:

> **BACTERIA + FOOD + MOISTURE + WARMTH + TIME = FOOD POISONING**

> **YOU CAN BREAK THIS CHAIN**

PERSONAL HYGIENE

Now you know that bacteria live in, and on, your own body, you can understand why it is so very important not only to keep yourself as clean as possible when working in the kitchen, but also to avoid bad habits which could encourage the spread of bacteria.

Always wash your hands

More than any other part of your body, your hands come into direct contact with food, and it is for this reason that they must be kept clean at all times.

Remember, one of the easiest ways for bacteria to spread through your kitchen is from your hands.

Thus it is important to **always wash your hands thoroughly**, using hot water, and soap (preferably liquid soap).

You must always wash your hands at proper hand-wash basins, NEVER at sinks in the kitchen itself, and it is just as important to dry your hands thoroughly, using a hot-air dryer, or disposable paper-towels. Use a clean, nylon-bristled nail-brush to clean your nails.

The times when you must wash your hands are:-

- before entering the kitchen and before touching any food
- after handling raw meat or poultry
- after using the lavatory
- after coughing into your hands or using a handkerchief
- after touching your face or hair
- after carrying out any cleaning

Always assume that raw meat and poultry are infected with bacteria, particularly salmonella bacteria, and that if you handle raw meat or poultry, and then go on to handle cooked meat, without first washing your hands, the cooked meat will almost certainly become infected through cross-contamination.

Your hands can carry bacteria that could kill if they ever found their way into food. Play safe — KEEP THEM CLEAN.

ALWAYS WASH YOUR HANDS
BEFORE HANDLING FOOD

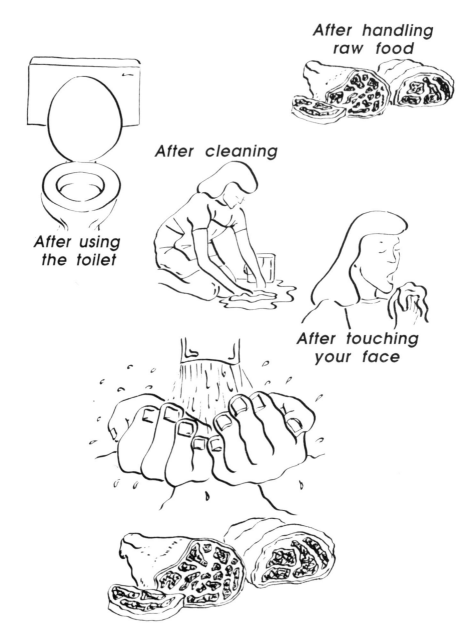

After handling
raw food

After cleaning

After using
the toilet

After touching
your face

Avoid bad habits

Because bacteria live in your nose, throat, mouth, and ears, you should avoid touching these areas.

Do not smoke in the kitchen: your hands can pick up bacteria either from your mouth or from cigarettes, and cigarette ash can fall into food.

Be aware of hair hygiene

Keep your hair covered with a net or disposable paper hat to prevent the bacteria that live in your hair and on your scalp from falling into food. Shampoo your hair frequently.

Keep your fingernails short

Short — and clean — fingernails offer less chance for bacteria to collect.

Do not wear jewellery

Bacteria and food can gather on items of jewellery, such as rings and bracelets.

Someone you know?

Keep all wounds covered with waterproof dressings

Remember that wounds, like cuts, grazes, scratches and boils, can quickly become infected with germs. The best way to prevent them from spreading to the food you handle, is to make sure that all such wounds are properly covered with a waterproof dressing.

Always wear clean protective clothing

Ensure that the clothes you wear in the kitchen are kept as clean as possible; clean overalls and aprons changed frequently is the correct procedure.

Report any illness

Should you feel unwell, report it to your supervisor or manager.

FOOD PREPARATION

Always keep raw meat and poultry away from cooked meat and poultry

It is very important to assume that raw meat, and especially raw poultry, is always infected with large numbers of bacteria. Regard the fluids that come from these meats as particularly dangerous. ALWAYS HANDLE WITH CARE.

Keep raw meat and raw poultry right away from other food — particularly from cooked meat and poultry — because it is so very easy for the bacteria to be transferred from the raw food into food nearby — this transfer is known as **Cross-Contamination**.

For example, bacteria will pass directly from a joint of contaminated raw meat to a joint of cooked meat, if the two joints come into contact with each other.

Also, a knife that is used to cut contaminated raw meat, will pick up bacteria and carry them over to the other foods with which it is used, if the knife is not first cleaned. This is indirect cross-contamination.

Preventing cross-contamination

Cross-contamination is a frequent result of carelessness. To prevent it from happening you should keep to the rules outlined below:-

- identify separate and distinct areas of the workplace for raw meat/poultry and for cooked food
- thoroughly clean the work surface where raw meat and poultry has been handled before preparing food in the same area
- wash thoroughly any kitchen utensils or equipment after they have been used with raw meat or poultry, and before they are used for anything else
- keep utensils used in the preparation of raw meats and poultry separate from those used for other foods. If possible adopt a system of **colour coding** under which items of equipment such as knives, chopping boards and cleaning cloths are given different coloured tags to show where in the work place the equipment is to be used and what it is to be used for

Colour coding reduces the risk of cross-contamination by ensuring that equipment is used only when and where it should be.

EXAMPLES OF COLOUR CODING	
Tag	Knives, chopping boards, cloths etc to be used only for
RED BLUE BROWN GREEN WHITE	Raw meat and poultry Fish Cooked meats Vegetables and fruit General purpose/bakery

Cook all food thoroughly

You will remember that bacteria are killed by heat, which is why it is so very important that food is cooked thoroughly — most bacteria will not survive in food that is cooked at a temperature of **75°C** for between **10–30 minutes**.

However, some forms of bacteria (spores) and some bacterial poisons (toxins) are only destroyed if cooked at higher temperatures for a greater length of time.

Special care should be taken to ensure that when food is re-heated after refrigeration, it is re-heated **thoroughly** at a high temperature, and that it is NEVER re-heated more than once.

To be cooked thoroughly, the centre, or core, of the food should be heated to a recommended temperature of **75°C**. To be sure that this core-temperature is reached in food that has been frozen, it is vital that larger portions of food be thawed thoroughly.

Clean all kitchen utensils thoroughly after use

As cutlery, chopping boards and other utensils are used repeatedly, you must ensure that all such equipment is cleaned regularly — before and after use. It would take only one piece of dirty equipment to contaminate all the food with which it was used.

Touch food as little as possible

Avoid touching food directly with your hands — as far as possible.

Use tongs, a suitable food bag, or plastic gloves to pick up items of food, and carry food only on trays or plates. This will reduce the risk of food being poisoned by any bacteria that your hands may carry.

Never test food with your fingers.

CLEAN ENVIRONMENT

Keep the kitchen clean

It is important that the workplace is also clean before you prepare food.

Dirt, rubbish, and waste food, not only carry bacteria, but encourage pests.

At the end of each day you should ensure that the following areas of the kitchen are clean:-

- floors
- walls
- windows
- work-surfaces
- ovens and grills

Keep waste bins covered — away from food

Waste food and rubbish will contain bacteria, so it is essential that it is kept well away from food preparation areas. Rubbish bins should remain covered at all times, and be regularly emptied, using disposable refuse bags.

It is important to remember that the points of food hygiene we have discussed here are all vital, and they will only be effective if you follow ALL of them at ALL times

Temperature Control

This important section specifies the action needed to avoid mistakes in the temperature control of food — the most common cause of problems.

TEMPERATURE AND BACTERIA

Because bacteria will grow rapidly in the Danger Zone (5°C—63°C) but cannot do so either at lower or higher temperatures, one of the most important aspects of food hygiene is temperature control.

Correct temperature control is a most powerful weapon against the infection of food by food poisoning bacteria

The rules of correct temperature control are quite simple, yet they are often misunderstood. For instance, a report has shown that in 1986 the majority of food poisoning cases were caused mostly by carelessness with temperature control.

The basic rules are:-

- keep hot food hot
- keep cold food cold
- keep prepared food out of the Danger Zone

Bacteria will grow rapidly in food that is left within the temperature Danger Zone, particularly in the "high risk" foods. For this reason, the idea behind correct temperature control is simply to keep food — above all the "high risk" foods — out of the Danger Zone whenever possible.

Thus, when food is cooked, it is essential that it is cooked **thoroughly**, to destroy any bacteria within. Once it has been prepared and is ready to be served, the temperature of the food must not be allowed to remain within the Danger Zone otherwise bacteria will be able to grow rapidly in the food.

For this reason cooked food should be served immediately. If it is not going to be eaten immediately, then it should be cooled rapidly and refrigerated until it is to be re-heated.

When food is re-heated, it should be done **thoroughly** to reach the cooking temperature. Warming refrigerated cooked poultry, and other meat and gravy, is bad practice and can be dangerous.

COOKING POULTRY

It is a bad idea to cook large poultry carcasses with the stuffing inside; the stuffing can prevent sufficient heat reaching the centre of the bird during cooking, so leaving food poisoning bacteria undestroyed. A better idea is to cook the poultry and the stuffing separately.

COOKING LARGE JOINTS OF MEAT

The larger the joint of meat, the longer it will take for the heat to reach the centre of the meat during cooking. Enough heat may reach the centre of the joint however to keep it within the "Danger Zone", so enabling food poisoning bacteria to grow rapidly.

Larger joints of meat should therefore be broken up into smaller pieces for cooking, so that sufficient heat to destroy bacteria will penetrate the centre of each piece much more quickly.

REFRIGERATORS

By keeping the food cold, at temperatures below 5°C, a refrigerator creates conditions in which there is little bacterial growth.

It is important to remember, however, that the temperature in a refrigerator does not prevent the growth of bacteria altogether, but can only delay it. Therefore, food should be placed in refrigeration only for short periods of time.

The food can be refrigerated for a maximum of 5 days (this includes the day of preparation and the day of consumption) after which it must be discarded.

The foods that should be refrigerated for short storage are:-

- raw meat and poultry
- fresh fish
- cooked meat and other foods to be eaten cold, or re-heated

- milk, and products containing milk
- cream, and products containing cream
- cheese, and products containing cheese
- eggs, and products containing eggs

Points to remember about refrigeration

- keep raw meat and poultry away from other food — especially cooked meat and cooked poultry
- NEVER place cooked food in the refrigerator immediately after cooking. Always allow it to cool first, covered, and away from all other food. Cooked meat and poultry should be cool enough to be placed in the refrigerator within 90 minutes of having been cooked
- keep all food covered as far as possible
- make sure that nothing — particularly raw meat and poultry — can drip on to food below

Always store raw meat and poultry *below* any food that will not be cooked before being eaten. In this way, such food cannot be contaminated by dripping juices.

- do not crowd food into the refrigerator — leave enough room for cold air to circulate

- defrost the refrigerator regularly to prevent the build-up of ice, and remember to keep it clean

- be sure that the refrigerator displays either a working temperature gauge, or a suitable thermometer, which must be checked daily to ensure that the temperature of the refrigerator is between 1°C and 4°C

- open refrigerator doors as infrequently as possible, and close them quickly

FREEZERS

Freezers keep food at a temperature well below freezing point. Some bacteria will die as a result of freezing, but others will survive, and although they are unable to grow at this temperature, they will do so when the temperature is raised.

The length of time food can be stored in a frozen state depends on the type of food and the rating of the freezing unit. It is important to check with the supplier of the food how long it can remain frozen.

Although frozen food may not become contaminated, it may suffer deterioration in flavour and character after a length of time, depending upon the type of food.

Points to remember about freezing

- the freezer should lower the temperature of the food to −22°C. The temperature of the freezer must not rise above −18°C

- all food should be wrapped

- all food should be placed neatly in the freezer

THAWING FOOD

Many foods can be taken from the freezer and cooked direct, without thawing. What is important to remember, however, is that **poultry, joints of meat** and **bulky items of food** MUST be completely thawed before cooking: unless complete thawing occurs, the temperature at the core of the food may not reach a high enough level during the cooking process to kill any bacteria that are present.

Food has been thoroughly thawed once it is soft, and there are no ice crystals present. When thawing frozen poultry, always assume that it carries large numbers of food poisoning bacteria.

Thawing can cause problems in that when the outer surface of the food warms up, bacteria can begin to grow, although the centre of the food remains frozen. With the centre frozen, the temperature reached by the cooking process is insufficient to kill any bacteria present at the centre of the food.

Food that is being thawed must not come into contact with food that is to be eaten without further cooking.

Thawing methods

For small joints and chickens, thawing can be carried out in the refrigerator. You must ensure that raw meat does not come into contact in the refrigerator with other food that is to be eaten without cooking.

As a rule, an average 3lb chicken should be allowed 24 hours to thaw, while a 16lb turkey would require 48 hours thawing time. The larger the joint or poultry carcass, the longer the thawing time that is required.

The method of thawing can also give rise to difficulties. Large turkeys and large joints of meat are not recommended for thawing in the ordinary domestic refrigerator because of the time it takes and the risk of contamination. Micro-wave ovens can sometimes be used, but they are not entirely satisfactory because the frozen food can thaw unevenly.

Sometimes the thawing process is speeded up by holding the poultry carcass or joint of meat under cold running water. However, when it is possible to do so, the most satisfactory method is to allow food to thaw in air, at a temperature around 15°C.

Points to remember about thawing raw meat and poultry

● place the frozen meat, poultry, or fish in a container and place in the refrigerator. If there is no available space in the refrigerator, place in a cool area of the kitchen that is not used for the preparation of other food. The container will catch any liquid that drains off from the food. You must ensure that this liquid does not come into contact with other food, utensils, or work-surfaces

● after thawing, make sure the food is cooked and eaten within 24 hours

● once frozen food has been thawed, NEVER RE-FREEZE IT!

A WORD ABOUT COOK-CHILL

Cook-chill is a system of catering that involves just what the name suggests; immediately after the food has been thoroughly cooked, it is rapidly chilled before being stored at a low temperature. The food is then re-heated **thoroughly** immediately before being eaten.

The main advantage of the cook-chill system is that because food is chilled so quickly after it has been cooked, there is no time for bacteria to grow. The system is being used increasingly in large scale catering, where entire meals can be stored fresh at the moment of chilling.

Some people question the safety of the cook-chill system, but like any other method of food preparation, it will be safe if the rules are obeyed precisely.

These rules are:-

● the chilling should begin within 30 minutes of the food having been cooked

● the food should be chilled rapidly to between 0°C and 3°C

● the chilling should be complete within 90 minutes

Refrigerators and freezers are NOT suitable for chilling — only purpose-built chilling equipment, known as a blast-chiller, should be used. Once the food has been chilled, then it must be transferred to a refrigerator.

The food should be stored for a maximum of 5 days (including the day of preparation and the day of consumption) after which it should be discarded. Chilled food that rises above 5°C should also be discarded.

Food that is to be re-heated should be re-heated IMMEDIATELY before being eaten, to a temperature of at least 75°C for between 10 minutes and 30 minutes — the larger the portion to be re-heated, the longer the re-heating should continue.

DRY FOOD STORAGE

All dry foods, such as flour, rice and pulses, and all canned food, should be stored in a room or cupboard that is **cool, dry, clean, and ventilated**.

All the food should be stored above floor level, on shelves out of reach of pests. Storage rooms and cupboards should be designed in such a way that pests have no way of getting in.

It is very important that you always rotate your stock so that the oldest food is used first. The longer food is stored, the greater is the chance of it becoming contaminated.

Make sure that food is not stored in a cramped or crowded fashion, so that you can see exactly which item of food should be used first.

One of the "golden rules" of food storage is to KEEP FOOD COVERED at all times. Food that is not pre-packed, such as rice, should be stored in metal bins, with tight fitting lids.

Most canned food will keep for anything up to 3 years. Poisoning from canned food is rare. Nevertheless, be sure to throw away any cans that are open, rusty, or dented.

Cleaning and Disinfection

This section describes some of the methods available for cleaning utensils and the work place.

CLEAN AS YOU GO

In working with food, it is almost inevitable that soiling of surfaces and utensils will occur. Thus it is important to establish a routine of cleaning. The maxim **"clean as you go"** is an excellent rule to follow. This also applies to dish-washing.

DISH-WASHING

Always aim to clean plates, cutlery and utensils immediately after use. This includes the containers and lids from food-trolleys, and any parts that can be dismantled from food-preparation machines such as mixers.

There are two ways of washing dishes — by hand, or by machine. Whichever method you use, the stages are the same:-

- removal of left-over food by scraping and rinsing
- washing in hot water with detergent. Detergents are intended to remove waste food and dirt from utensils and equipment
- rinsing and drying

Washing by hand

The most hygienic way to hand-wash is with TWO stainless-steel sinks side by side.

If you do not have two sinks in your work place, you can either clean and then rinse in the same sink, or rinse in a separate bowl of hot water. The rinse water should be changed frequently, when dirty or cooled. Rinsing is important. Laboratory tests have shown that dishes which are not rinsed are covered with large numbers of bacteria.

Adopt the following steps in dish-washing: —

● wear rubber gloves
This will protect your hands from scalding and the effects of detergents and chemical disinfectant

● remove left-over food
This can be done by scraping and rinsing under running water

● wash in hot water and detergent
In the first sink, items are placed into hot water (about 50°C) and detergent, and scrubbed with a tough, nylon-bristled brush

● rinse in very hot water
In the second sink, (or both) items are rinsed in very hot water (70°C-80°C) before being stacked to dry
As well as killing bacteria and removing detergent, rinsing in this way makes the items hot enough to dry quickly on contact with the air, so avoiding the need of drying-up cloths which can spread bacteria if they are allowed to become dirty

● dry
After rinsing, the items should be left to drain in a clean, dry area, well away from any dirty washing water, until they are clean, dry and without smears

Washing by machine

There are several types of dish and utensil-washing machines available and they all follow the stages of cleaning just mentioned — i.e. plates, cutlery and utensils are washed in hot water and detergent, and then rinsed and disinfected with hot water sprays, or steam.

In a machine the hot water and detergent should be between 49°C and 60°C.

The rinsing water should be between 66°C and 80°C. Steam can be used to disinfect.

Whether the items to be washed pass through the machine on a moving belt, or you load them in baskets into large cabinets, it is important that they are stacked neatly so that the detergent and the hot water can reach them. Cups, glasses and jugs should be stacked upside-down, to avoid collecting water.

Whichever kind of machine you use, it will only clean effectively if the washing and rinsing occur at the correct temperature. A washing machine that does not operate properly is a hazard.

CHEMICAL DISINFECTION

Disinfection by heat is the most effective way of killing off bacteria during cleaning, but **chemical disinfectants** can be used in addition, or in situations where hot water is not available. However they are less effective in water that is not hot.

It is a popular myth that the use of disinfectants achieves perfect cleanliness. Chemical disinfectants are not as effective as good cleaning with hot water and detergent. They are useful in reducing the numbers of bacteria on surfaces that come into contact with food, as well as for floors and toilet areas, but care must be taken to ensure that the food itself does not become contaminated by the disinfectants.

A variety of chemical agents are available, generally either in powder or liquid form. Only small concentrations need usually be added to the wash water, but it is important to follow the instructions for use.

Chemical disinfectants are intended to kill bacteria, but a few are always likely to survive. Nevertheless, if used properly, chemical disinfectants can help to reduce the number of bacteria to safe levels.

Sanitisers are chemicals designed to remove waste food and kill food poisoning bacteria. They tend to be less effective than disinfectant in destroying all bacteria, but play a useful role in cleaning.

CLEANING THE WORKPLACE

Work-surfaces

It is vital that surfaces upon which food is prepared are kept clean and bacteria-free for each new job.

Work-surfaces, ovens and grills should be scrubbed, using a bowl of hot water and detergent, with a second bowl of hot rinsing water — both should be changed when they begin to appear dirty.

A disinfectant can be of use in killing bacteria.

After scrubbing, the surfaces must be dried with clean, absorbent, disposable paper towels.

Floors

Floors can be cleaned thoroughly and quickly with electric floor scrubbers.

A tankful of hot water and detergent is fed down to a large scrubbing disk. The detergent suds can then be sucked up by an electric floor dryer.

If you do not have a machine, small areas can be scrubbed by hand using a tough bristled brush and a bowl of hot water and detergent. Finish off by rinsing with a mop using hot water that will dry on contact with the air.

When sweeping the floor, wrap a clean, damp cloth around the brush-head, to avoid raising dust.

Always walk backwards to avoid stepping on areas you have cleaned, but take care to avoid injury either to yourself or others. If possible, put out hazard cones or notices to warn that the floor is wet.

Ceilings and walls

Ceilings and walls should be wiped with a clean damp cloth, using a detergent. A steriliser should be used for areas where splashes and stains may occur — such as immediately behind sinks or work surfaces.

A warning!

YOU SHOULD NEVER ATTEMPT TO MIX
DIFFERENT CLEANING CHEMICALS

To do so could result in a mixture that produces poisonous gases.

Kitchen Design and Layout

This section describes the standard of workplace which you should expect. Much of what is said is also relevant to the domestic kitchen.

THE HYGIENIC KITCHEN

The design and layout of your kitchen can directly affect the level of food hygiene that you can achieve; a kitchen that is badly designed and poorly set out will make it that much more difficult to prevent the contamination of food.

Basically, a hygienic kitchen layout is one that allows plenty of space for work and storage, where food preparation can be clearly organized.

Work surfaces

As work surfaces are constantly in use, they must be strong, durable, and easily cleaned. Stainless steel tables with hollow steel legs are ideal. Castors with brakes on the legs of work surfaces and on the bottom of smaller items of machinery are a good idea, as they allow the work surfaces and machines to be moved out of the way when the floor is being cleaned.

It is important that all areas of the kitchen be well lit so that you can see clearly what you are doing, as well as being able to see what is present in the kitchen around you.

Floors

A kitchen floor must be durable, easy to clean, non-absorbent, and non-slip. It must have as few crevices as possible, as these provide good sites for bacteria. It must also be resistant to any acids, fat, or grease that may spill on to it.

Given these requirements, wood is particularly unsuitable as a material for a kitchen floor — it is absorbent, it splinters and cracks easily, and wears quickly.

More suitable are quarry tiles, but these must be laid carefully as crevices tend to appear between tiles.

Ideally, floors should be made from thick, non-slip vinyl sheets. Care must be taken to ensure that the floor is coved where it meets the wall, to prevent bacteria and pests from moving in under the skirting.

Walls

Like the floor, the walls should be smooth and free from cracks and crevices — smooth plaster provides a suitable surface, with glazed tiles being used in those areas where the walls are likely to be splashed — such as behind sinks and above work surfaces. Walls should be painted a light colour, to show up any dirt or grease, using a quality, heat and steam resistant emulsion.

Ceilings

Likewise, ceilings should be smooth, light in colour, and fire-resistant. Either solid or suspended fibre-board ceilings should be coved where they meet the walls.

It is vital that there be an adequate ventilation system that allows fresh air to circulate through the kitchen, generally through short ducts in the ceiling. Extractor fans can be used in smaller kitchens.

Lighting

Good artificial lighting is necessary to show up dirt on equipment and surfaces, and will help to prevent accidents.

Toilet and washing facilities

Everyone working in the kitchen must have access to toilet facilities — but toilets should be situated well away from the kitchen itself, in a room that is reached by crossing a well ventilated corridor or lobby.

Toilets should be well ventilated and should contain at least one hand-wash basin, with either a roll-towel dispenser, paper-towel dispenser, or hot-air dryer. Wrist operated taps are recommended to reduce the risk of cross-contamination from the hands.

It is essential to situate wash basins near the door, with a clearly visible "NOW WASH YOUR HANDS" notice nearby.

There should be at least one hand-wash basin in the kitchen, but this should be well away from any food preparation areas.

All hand-wash basins should have hot and cold running water, and be supplied with liquid soap and nylon-bristle nail brushes. The liquid soap containers should be cleaned and disinfected when empty, and nail brushes should be cleaned at the end of each day.

Waste disposal

Waste food can be disposed of efficiently and immediately in purpose-built waste disposal machines that break the food down before flushing it away through a waste pipe.

Any waste food or refuse that is not disposed of mechanically should be sealed in durable plastic bags and placed in galvanized iron bins, with close-fitting lids.

These refuse bins should be stored well away from food preparation areas — ideally outside the kitchen — in their own storage area, which should have a concrete floor that is regularly hosed down with water. The refuse bins themselves should be emptied frequently and cleaned regularly.

WORK FLOW

Organizing the kitchen into separate areas for separate jobs lies at the heart of hygienic kitchen design. The exact layout will depend upon the size of the kitchen, as well as the type of meals it prepares, but work must flow smoothly:

DELIVERY → STORAGE → PREPARATION → SERVICE

Storage rooms and refrigerators and freezers should be near delivery areas.

Vegetables and fruits should be prepared near their place of storage, away from other preparation areas, to prevent the spread of soil.

Raw meat and poultry should be prepared well away from areas where other foods are prepared.

Preparation sites should be situated around the sides of the kitchen, with cooking equipment grouped in "islands" at the centre, beneath central ventilation ducts.

By organizing the kitchen in this way, the risk of placing raw food near cooked food, or of placing waste near food preparation areas, is greatly reduced.

CORRECT SEPARATION OF FOOD

KEEP SEPARATE

 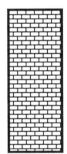 

Raw food   *Cooked food*

EXAMPLE OF THE LAYOUT OF A HYGIENIC CATERING KITCHEN

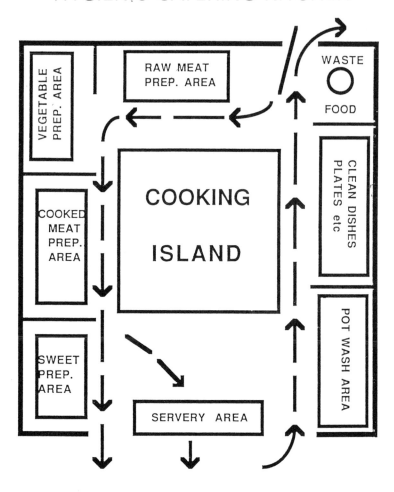

SEPARATION OF 'CLEAN' AND 'DIRTY' AREAS

Pest Control

This section tells you what expert help should be sought for pest control, but also outlines limited action which you can take.

PESTS AND FOOD

Pests that are commonly found in places where food is prepared or stored for human consumption are of three varieties:-

- RODENTS — such as mice and rats
- INSECTS — such as houseflies, cockroaches, ants and a variety of other insects associated with food
- BIRDS — such as wild pigeons and sparrows

The problems caused by these pests is not just that they eat and spoil food, but that they can also carry food poisoning bacteria.

Many of these pests live and feed in places where food poisoning bacteria are found, carrying them on their bodies and transferring them to food.

Many pests such as rats, mice and flies, also carry food poisoning bacteria in their intestines, which they pass in their excreta and which can then get into food.

PREVENTIVE MEASURES

Pests require food, warmth and shelter, thus it is important to ensure that as far as possible, pests do not have access to premises where food is stored or prepared. If, however, in spite of precautions in making the building proof against pests, they still gain access, you should make the workplace as unattractive and inaccessible to them as possible, with the following measures:-

- keep your workplace clean
- clear-up any food that spills on to the floor
- keep waste food in covered refuse bins
- store dry and perishable foods in closely covered metal bins
- check deliveries for pests

SPOTTING PESTS

Always look out for the following signs:-

- live or dead bird, insect or rodent bodies
- droppings
- torn sacks or bags
- holes in cardboard boxes and containers

It is important in the design of premises to prevent access to pests that generally come from outside, by ensuring there are no crevices or neglected areas of the workplace in which they can be harboured.

GETTING RID OF PESTS

If you are unfortunate enough to find any of these signs, or to realise that your workplace is infested, then the general rule is to seek expert advice. This can be obtained from the Environmental Health Department of the local authority, or from specialised private contractors.

The main steps that are taken are:-

- trapping and catching pests such as rodents and insects
- fitting "insectocutors" — electrified ultra-violet tube-lighting — which kill flies and other flying insects that come into contact with them. The dead insects fall into a collecting tray
- laying poisons. Poisons must be handled with great care and always be kept away from food. However, they· are very useful weapons in expert hands for dealing with the pests that are found in food preparation and storage areas

> **KEEP POISONS AWAY FROM FOOD**

Food Hygiene and the Law

This section picks out a few points of concern to you from the large amount of law concerning food hygiene.

THE LAW

There are several sets of Acts and regulations that have been designed to protect the public against food that is unfit to eat.

The Food Hygiene (General) Regulations 1970, are those most directly concerned with protecting the public against outbreaks of food poisoning. These regulations set out the rules of food hygiene applicable to every establishment that prepares and/or sells food to the public.

Such regulations are enforced by the Local Authority of your district, and failure to abide by them could result in your prosecution — which could mean a fine or even a term of imprisonment, depending on the seriousness of the offence. Given below is a brief summary of some of the more important regulations.

THE PREMISES

The premises on which food is prepared and/or sold, must reach a satisfactory level of hygiene in its construction, layout, and over-all condition.

This means that the kitchen, and other areas where food is stored, served, or sold, must be:-

- kept clean
- properly equipped
- properly organized
- well lit and well ventilated
- free from the accumulation of waste and refuse
- supplied with toilets situated in a room separate from food areas
- equipped with areas for the storage of food handlers' personal clothes

WASHING AND TOILET FACILITIES

The premises must have a clean supply of water, with facilities for washing food, utensils and equipment.

Kitchen sinks and hand-wash basins must have a clean supply of hot and cold running water.

Hand-wash basins must be used by food handlers only to wash their hands, and must be provided with soap, nail-brushes, and clean towels or hot air-dryers.

Wash and toilet rooms must be kept clean and in good repair. They must be well lit, well ventilated, and should carry notices asking that after using the toilet, employees should wash their hands.

EQUIPMENT

All food equipment must be kept clean, and in good working order.

FOOD HANDLERS

It is the direct responsibility of the food handler to guard against the contamination of food, by following the rules of food hygiene.

Food handlers must:-

- keep themselves clean
- wear clean overalls
- follow the rules of personal and general hygiene

CATERING PRACTICE

Meat, fish, gravy, imitation cream, egg, or foods prepared from or containing these foods, must be kept at temperatures either below 10°C or above 62.8°C.

Note: Although at present the Food Hygiene (General) Regulations 1970 require these foods to be kept below 10°C (or above 62.8°C) current discussions indicate that at the lower end a safer temperature would be 5°C. See Section 12.

Update

This section deals with some of the important things which have occurred since the booklet was first written.

RECENT EVENTS

During the latter part of 1988 and early 1989 there was massive media attention to the problem of food poisoning.

Not only were reported cases of food poisoning continuing to increase but, additionally, there were alarming reports of eggs being infected by a strain of **salmonella** and of certain foods being affected by **listeria,** a bacteria little known to the general public. Grist to the mill of publicity was added by accusations of a ''cover up'' by Government departments.

How much do these happenings affect the advice given in the earlier Sections?

Well, not a lot.

Nevertheless it is worth reviewing the evidence. The media concern related mainly to infection at the production stage of the food chain. Although this is largely outside the responsibility of the food handler it does emphasise the need for greater care in handling potentially infected raw food. By acting in accordance with the rules you can prevent the infection being passed on to the consumer.

SALMONELLA AND EGGS

Salmonella infection in eggs is not new. The cautionary tale at Section 1 is one example. Recently, there has been a real increase in the number of cases associated with salmonella-infected eggs in this and other countries. It is difficult to be certain on how big the increase really is because the strain of salmonella (enteriditis phage type 4) responsible for the infection of eggs is also found in poultry meat. But probably there has been at least a doubling of the amount of food poisoning attributable to infected eggs.

In the first three months of 1989 about 1500 cases (U.K.) of food poisoning caused by this particular strain of salmonella were notified and many more, probably as many as ten times more, would go unreported. Even so, when one considers that some of these cases would be due to poultry meat—not eggs—and that around 30 million eggs are eaten in Britain each day, the overall risk is small. But it must be guarded against.

Eggs may be infected with salmonella bacteria in a number of ways:-

- there may be bacteria adhering to the shell which get inside when the egg is broken (or becomes cracked)
- the bacteria may be inside the hen and be implanted within the egg prior to its being laid
- the germs can be absorbed through the shell—especially a moist, warm shell

It is very difficult to detect salmonella in individual eggs. Of many thousands tested, very few have been found to be infected. However when eggs are pooled the bacteria from even a few eggs will spread quickly through the bulk and salmonella will be found in the dried or liquid products unless they are heat treated. This is why it is necessary, if using powdered or liquid eggs, to use a pasteurised product.

Salmonella are readily killed by heat. At 70°C nearly all are killed after three or four minutes. Thus if the rules of food hygiene are followed there should be no risk to the consumer.

Points to remember about eggs

- wash your hands before and after handling eggs
- do not store or use cracked eggs
- store eggs in cool dry conditions, for preference under refrigeration
- avoid cross contamination. Raw egg can contaminate other food or be contaminated by other food
- avoid using raw shell egg in recipes where no cooking, or only light cooking, is involved
- cook eggs adequately
- eat egg dishes as soon as possible after preparation or keep them under refrigeration.

LISTERIA AND FOOD

Listeria monocytogenes (to use the full name) are small bacteria found in water, soil, vegetation and in the intestines of many domestic and wild animals such as dogs, foxes, chickens, rats, sheep, goats and cattle. The bacteria can be passed into the milk of infected animals. One in twenty people carry it in their gut, usually without being aware of this. Hence all of us have had contact with this bacteria and for the vast majority it causes no harm when swallowed.

Two groups of people are identified as being at risk: a small group of patients whose illness or treatment affects their immune system and women who are pregnant in whom on rare occasions it can result in a miscarriage.

Listeria have been found in large numbers in certain soft ripened cheeses and these should be avoided by those two groups of people.

Small numbers of listeria have been isolated from about one in ten samples of pre-cooked poultry and about one in five cook-chill meals. However the listeria are easily destroyed by adequate reheating. Salads prepared in dressings (eg coleslaw) and vegetables may also harbour listeria.

Listeria is unusual in that it can grow in the refrigerator — albeit slowly — at temperatures which would be too cold for other bacteria to do so.

Points to remember regarding listeria

- cook food adequately and the bacteria will be killed
- reheat food once only and ensure it is heated all the way through until piping hot. Dispose of left over reheated food
- follow the storage instructions carefully and observe "eat by" dates on labels
- wash salads, fruit and vegetables if these are to be eaten raw

CAMPYLOBACTER INFECTIONS

One further food poisoning bacteria, **campylobacter,** is worthy of mention. Over the years, the media has not paid a great deal of attention to campylobacter but the bacteria is now emerging as an important source of food poisoning. Since the early 1980's the reported cases of campylobacter infections have exceeded those for salmonella. In 1988 there were almost 29,000 reported cases in England and Wales of campylobacter infection and many more cases would go unreported. (See figure next page)

Campylobacter and Salmonella Infections 1980−1988

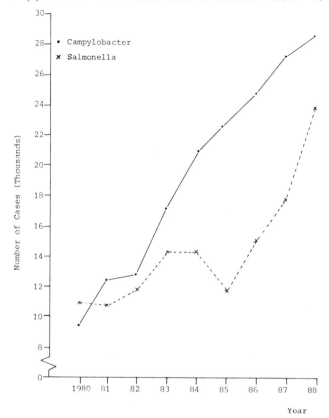

In the 1970's the development of new laboratory techniques allowed detailed examination of this group of bacteria. The importance of this work resulted in these bacteria being recognised as a separate family and given the name campylobacter.

The name campylobacter is derived from Greek − *kampulos* meaning curved and *bakterion* meaning a rod. This is because the bacteria are slim rods, spiral or "S" shaped which can move rapidly in fluid. They are smaller than most other bacteria found in the intestine. They have been found in the intestines and faeces of a wide range of animals including pets and domestic animals, dogs, cats, cattle, sheep, chickens and cage birds.

The way the infection is spread to humans is very similar to that in which salmonella is spread i.e. mainly from the bacteria being present in raw foods of animal origin−with, once again, poultry being high on the list.

53

So if you follow the rules in the booklet about handling the "high-risk" foods safely and remember the "danger zone" there should be few problems from campylobacter infection. Practise what you have read about thorough cooking, refrigeration, thawing, personal hygiene and avoiding cross-contamination—these will usually take care of any danger in the kitchen from campylobacter.

However there are some additional sources of infection. Unpasteurised milk has been implicated in outbreaks as have water supplies in some overseas countries. Indeed, in this country, campylobacter has been isolated from coastal sea water.

TEMPERATURE CONTROL

Great emphasis has already been placed on the importance of temperature control. You know that the law identifies a wide range of foods which must be kept at temperatures below 10°C or above 62.8°C—because in between lies the Danger Zone.

However, for a long time it has been known from research that under certain conditions some harmful bacteria can grow at temperatures as low as 5°C. For example, a study showed that salmonella could multiply on cooked chicken at 7°C. With listeria some growth can occur at an even lower temperature but below 5°C there is no major risk.

Thus the really safe lower temperature is 5°C rather than the 10°C which the law currently lays down. No doubt the law will eventually be changed to take this into account.

**REGARD THE DANGER ZONE AS
5°C to 63°C**

Finally, please do remember each day to check, using a reliable thermometer, that the temperature in the refrigerator is beween 1°C-4°C.

"WHAT SHOULD I DO?"

"Why should I do it?"

WASH YOUR HANDS

- after using the lavatory
- between handling raw meat and cooked meat
- before and after touching food
- after coughing into your hands or using a handkerchief
- after touching your face or hair
- after carrying out any cleaning

There are many bacteria on the surface of your skin. Most are harmless, but some, when transferred to food, can cause illness. In addition your hands can pick up bacteria from other sources and contaminate food

AVOID TOUCHING YOUR NOSE, COUGHING OR SNEEZING OVER FOOD

Personal cleanliness is vital, otherwise you will add your own bacteria to the food

AVOID TOUCHING FOOD WITH YOUR HANDS. WHENEVER POSSIBLE USE TONGS TO HANDLE FOOD AND PLATES OR TRAYS TO CARRY IT

The less your hands are in direct contact with food, the less chance there is of contamination occurring

KEEP HAIR COVERED WITH A NET OR DISPOSABLE HAT

Your hair and scalp carry many bacteria which can fall into food

KEEP FINGERNAILS SHORT AND CLEAN

Bacteria can collect beneath long nails, and pass into the food you handle

KEEP CUTS, GRAZES AND BOILS COVERED WITH A WATERPROOF DRESSING THAT IS BRIGHTLY COLOURED — BLUE IS A GOOD COLOUR

Wounds such as these are often infected with bacteria. They must be properly covered to prevent the spread of bacteria. Brightly coloured dressings will be easily spotted if they fall into food

"WHAT SHOULD I DO?"	"Why should I do it?"
KEEP RAW AND COOKED FOOD SEPARATE, ESPECIALLY RAW MEAT/POULTRY AND COOKED MEAT/POULTRY	Play safe! Always regard raw meat and poultry as contaminated. Don't spread infection
CLEAN KITCHEN UTENSILS AND EQUIPMENT THOROUGHLY, BEFORE AND AFTER USE	There is always the risk in the workplace that utensils and equipment can become contaminated with bacteria
KEEP FOOD AT THE CORRECT TEMPERATURE — IN STORAGE AND PREPARATION ★ REMEMBER THE "HIGH RISK" FOODS ★ REMEMBER THE TEMPERATURE "DANGER ZONE"	High risk foods (eg meat, poultry, gravy etc) provide bacteria with the nutrients and moisture needed to grow. In the temperature "Danger Zone" (5°C to 63°C) bacteria multiply at a very fast rate
BE SURE THAT CERTAIN FROZEN FOOD IS THAWED THOROUGHLY BEFORE COOKING — ESPECIALLY POULTRY AND LARGE JOINTS OF MEAT	Thorough thawing is essential if the centre of the food is to reach the temperature required to destroy bacteria during cooking
KEEP FOOD COVERED WHENEVER POSSIBLE	To protect it against contamination
ALWAYS ENSURE THAT THE WORKPLACE IS CLEAN BEFORE PREPARING FOOD	Thorough cleaning is necessary to kill any bacteria already present

ANNUAL INCIDENCE (of food poisoning)	The total number of NEW cases of food poisoning in one year.
BACTERIA	Tiny living creatures, invisible to the naked eye. Food poisoning bacteria cause the symptoms of food poisoning.
COOK-CHILL	A catering system in which food is cooked, and within 90 minutes cooled to 3°C, in a blast-chiller and stored between 0°C and 3°C.
CROSS-CONTAMINATION	The transfer of food poisoning bacteria from contaminated food to raw food or cold cooked food.
DANGER ZONE	The temperature range within which bacteria grow most quickly. (5°C to 63°C)
DETERGENT	A chemical used during the cleaning of utensils, equipment and work surfaces. It will remove waste food and dirt, but will not destroy food poisoning bacteria when used alone.
DISINFECTANT	A chemical designed to kill food poisoning bacteria—used during the cleaning of floors, drains and toilets.
FOOD POISONING	An illness caused by eating food that has become poisonous; the main symptoms are diarrhoea, vomiting and stomach pains.
HIGH RISK FOODS	The foods most at risk from bacterial infection because they provide the nutrients that bacteria need to grow.
SALMONELLA	The family of bacteria responsible for a large proportion of the food poisoning outbreaks in Great Britain.
SANITISER	A chemical designed to remove waste food AND destroy bacteria.

THE ROYAL SOCIETY OF HEALTH

The Society is for men and women having a professional interest in one of the following:-

- health care
- environment and hygiene
- nutrition
- social services

There are four grades of membership:-

- Fellow   (FRSH)
- Member   (MRSH)
- Associate Member   (AMRSH)
- Affiliate   (Affil RSH)

Election to a particular grade of membership is dependent upon the qualifications of the applicant. The list of recognised qualifications includes those in environmental health, hygiene, catering and nutrition.

The Journal of the Society is issued free to members — 6 issues each year — and there are reduced fees for conferences and free attendance at lectures.

Requests for information on membership should be sent, accompanied by details of qualifications held, to:-

The Secretary
RSH House
38A St George's Drive
London SW1V 4BH

(Tel: 01 630 0121)